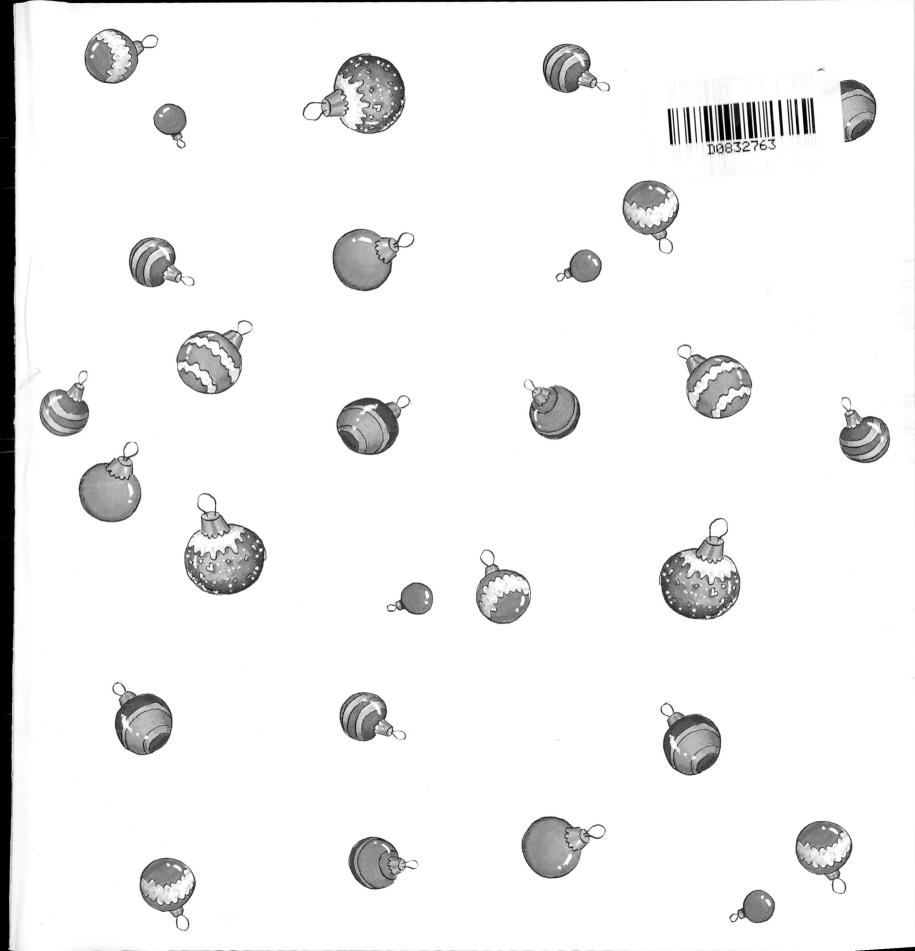

To Henrietta Clark, whose passion for quality children's television has made an incalculable contribution
to the lives of millions—me included!   – CB

To Kyle who watched me colour, little Dion Kelly . . . and to Angie M and Eve T for your patience.   – GS

Scholastic Australia
345 Pacific Highway Lindfield NSW 2070
An imprint of Scholastic Australia Pty Limited
PO Box 579 Gosford NSW 2250
ABN 11 000 614 577
www.scholastic.com.au

Part of the Scholastic Group
Sydney • Auckland • New York • Toronto • London • Mexico City • New Delhi • Hong Kong • Buenos Aires • Puerto Rico

Published by Scholastic Australia in 2012.
All words by Colin Buchanan © 2012 Universal Music Publishing Australia P/L.
Illustrations copyright © Glen Singleton, 2012.

National Library of Australia Cataloguing-in-Publication entry

Author:	Buchanan, Colin, 1964-
Title:	Twelve days of Aussie Christmas / written by Colin Buchanan
	and illustrated by Glen Singleton.
ISBN:	9781742833675 (hbk.)
Target Audience:	For pre-school age.
Subjects:	Christmas stories, Australian.
Other Authors/Contributors:	Singleton, Glen, 1959-
Dewey Number:	A823.4

Typeset in Stanyan.

Printed in China by RR Donnelley.

Scholastic Australia's policy, in association with RR Donnelley, is to use papers that are renewable and made efficiently from wood grown in sustainable
forests, so as to minimise its environmental footprint.

10 9 8 7 6 5 4 3 2 1   12 13 14 15 16 / 1

The Twelve Days of Aussie Christmas

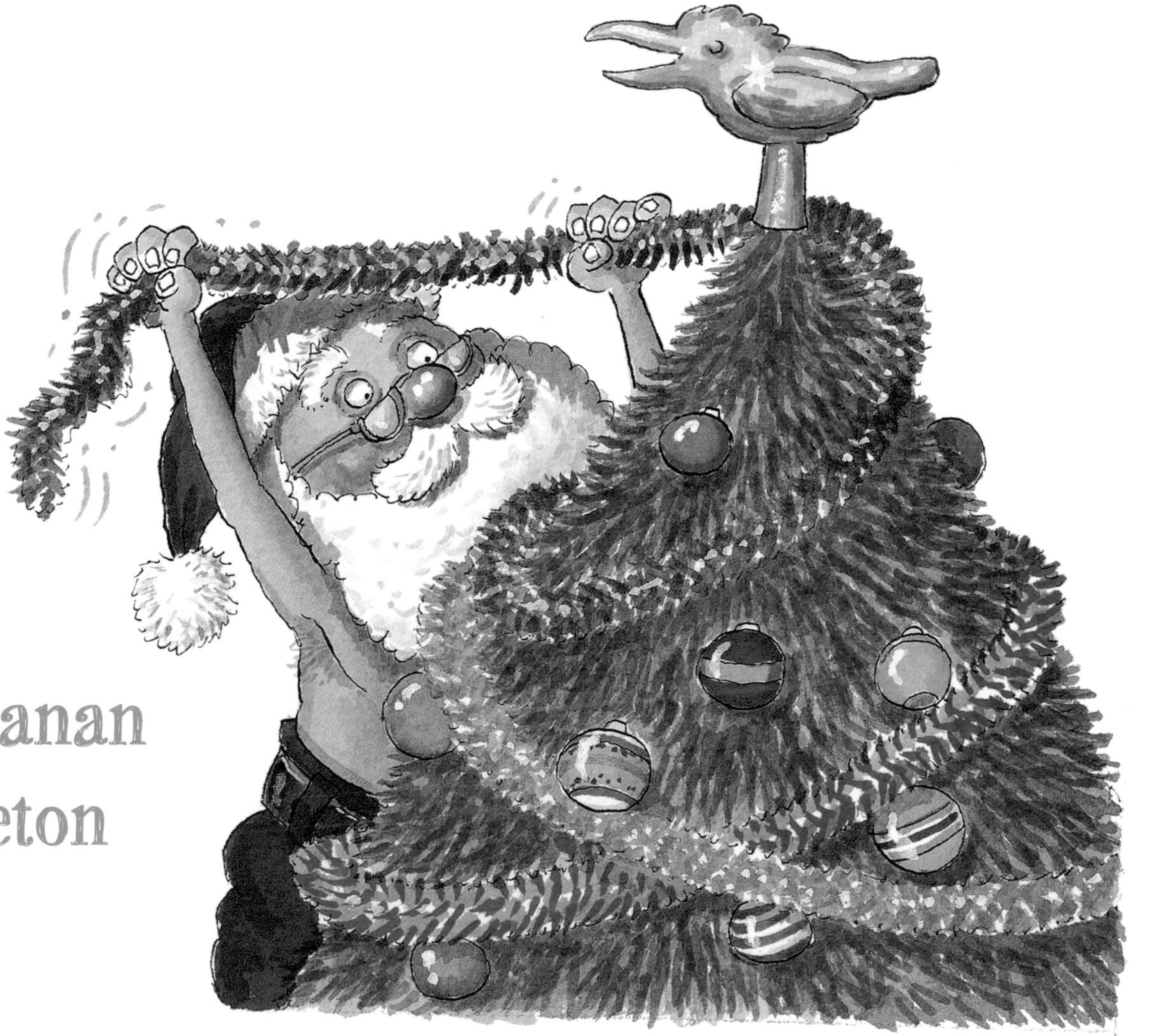

Colin Buchanan

Glen Singleton

A Scholastic Australia Book

On the first day of Christmas, my best mate gave to me . . .
A platypus up a gum tree.

On the second day of Christmas, my best mate gave to me . . .

Two jackaroos,

And a platypus up a gum tree.

On the third day of Christmas, my best mate gave to me . . .

Three meat trays,

Two jackaroos,

And a platypus up a gum tree.

On the fourth day of Christmas, my best mate gave to me . . .

Four footy fans,
Three meat trays,
Two jackaroos,
And a platypus up a gum tree.

On the fifth day of Christmas, my best mate gave to me . . .

Five rusty utes!

Four footy fans,
Three meat trays,
Two jackaroos,
And a platypus up a gum tree.

On the sixth day of Christmas, my best mate gave to me . . .
Half a dozen snags,
Five rusty utes!
Four footy fans,
Three meat trays,
Two jackaroos,
And a platypus up a gum tree.

On the seventh day of Christmas, my best mate gave to me . . .
Seven cheeky chooks,
Half a dozen snags,
Five rusty utes!
Four footy fans,
Three meat trays,
Two jackaroos,

And a platypus up a gum tree.

On the eighth day of Christmas, my best mate gave to me . . .

Eight jolly jumbucks,
Seven cheeky chooks,
Half a dozen snags,
Five rusty utes!
Four footy fans,
Three meat trays,
Two jackaroos,

And a platypus up a gum tree.

On the ninth day of Christmas, my best mate gave to me . . .
Nine daggy dingos,

Eight jolly jumbucks,
Seven cheeky chooks,
Half a dozen snags,
Five rusty utes!
Four footy fans,
Three meat trays,
Two jackaroos,
And a platypus up a gum tree.

On the tenth day of Christmas, my best mate gave to me . . .

Ten sweaty swaggies,

Nine daggy dingos,

Eight jolly jumbucks,

Seven cheeky chooks,

Half a dozen snags,

Five rusty utes!

Four footy fans,

Three meat trays,

Two jackaroos,

And a platypus up a gum tree.

On the eleventh day of Christmas, my best mate gave to me . . .
Eleven cricket legends,
Ten sweaty swaggies,
Nine daggy dingos,
Eight jolly jumbucks,
Seven cheeky chooks,
Half a dozen snags,
Five rusty utes!
Four footy fans,
Three meat trays,
Two jackaroos,
And a platypus up a gum tree.

On the twelfth day of Christmas, my best mate gave to me . . .

Twelve surfing Santas,
Eleven cricket legends,
Ten sweaty swaggies,
Nine daggy dingos,
Eight jolly jumbucks,
Seven cheeky chooks,
Half a dozen snags,

Five rusty utes!
Four footy fans,
Three meat trays,
Two jackaroos . . .

And a platypus up a gum tree!

LOOK and FIND LIST

12 glittery gumnuts

11 buzzing baubles

10 peeking possums

9 fleeting finches

8 frilled neck lizards

7 balancing bush rats

6 yuletide yabbies

5 red-nosed boomers

4 giddy goannas

3 tinsel Tassies

2 Christmas crocodiles

1 shiny kookaburra

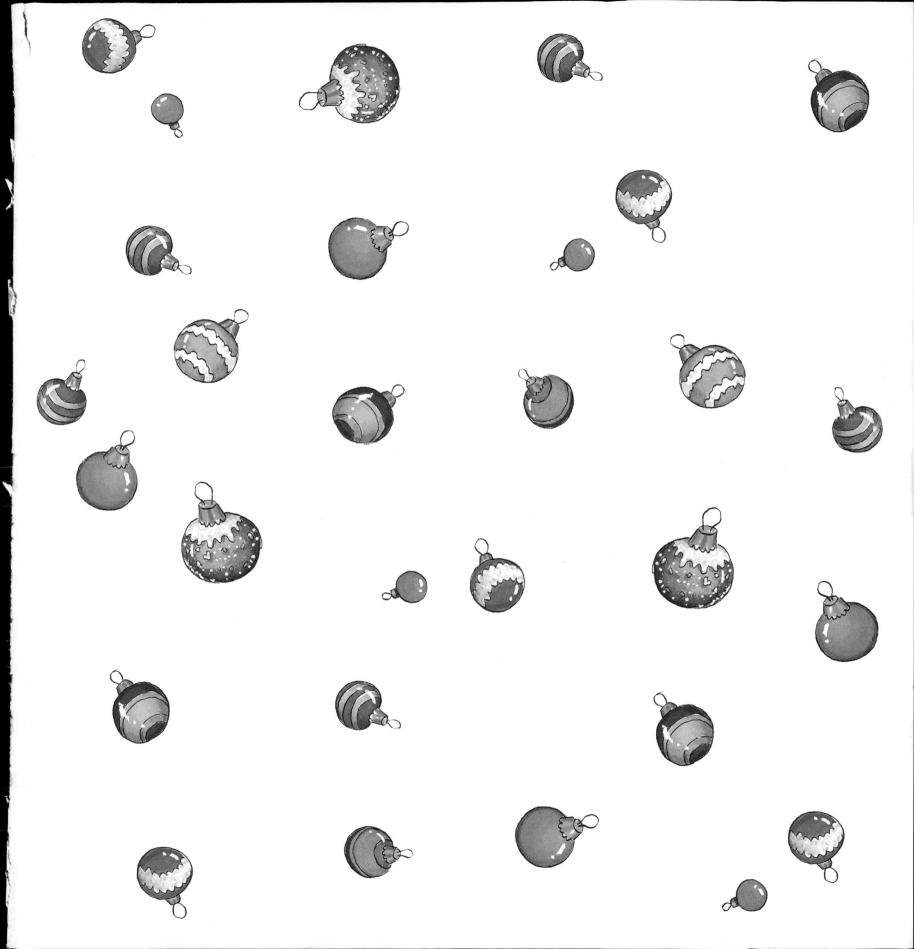

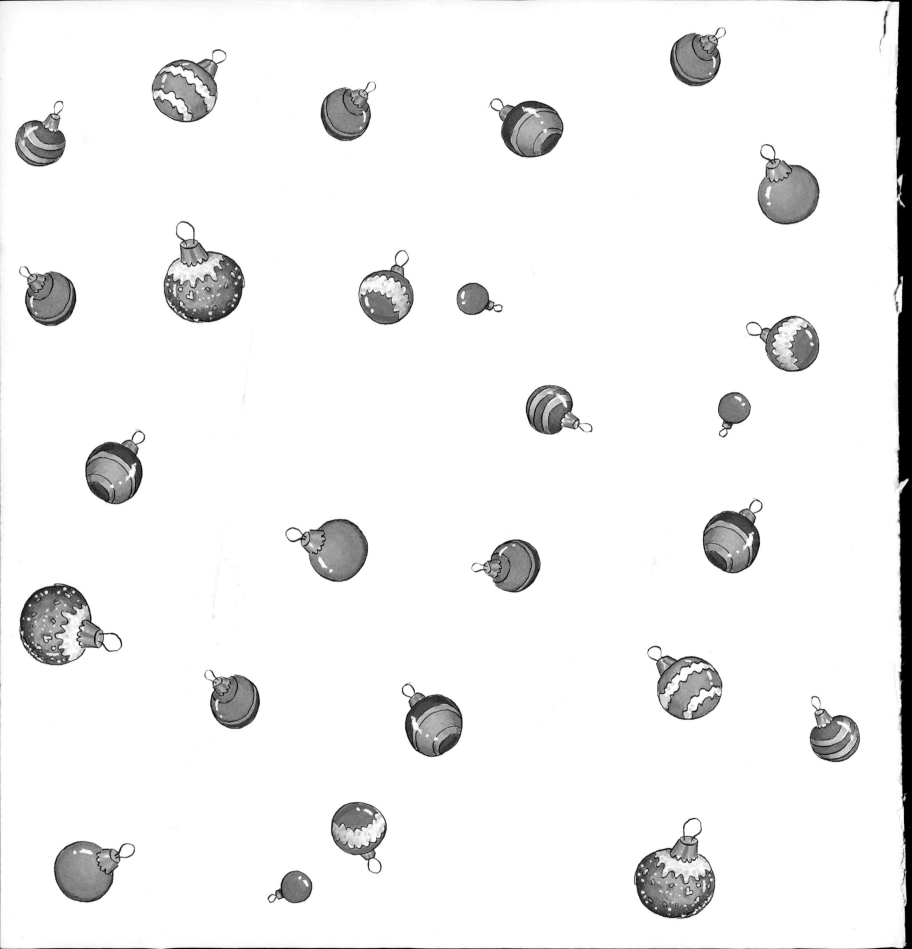